WRITING FRAMES

40 Activities for Learning the Writing Process

Jean L. Pottle

J. Weston Walch, Publisher
Portland, Maine

5   6   7   8   9   10

ISBN 0-8251-1564-7

Copyright © 1988

J. Weston Walch, Publisher

P.O. Box 658 • Portland, Maine 04104-0658

Printed in the United States of America

Contents

To the Teacher . . . v

First Quarter Writing Frames

Second Quarter Writing Frames

Third Quarter Writing Frames

Fourth Quarter Writing Frames

To the Teacher

A writing frame is a partially completed paragraph which offers writing ideas to students while encouraging them to incorporate their own ideas and words into the frame. Writing frames may be used in a variety of ways in the language classroom. They may be used as a brainstorming technique, as a simple writing activity which supplies a model for student writers, or as a rough draft for a finished piece. This workbook can be the basis of an entire year's writing program, or the frames may be used individually as need demands.

However the frames are used, the objective for their use remains the same: to gradually convince students that they can write, and to teach them the techniques needed to develop ideas. If frames are used on a regular basis, you will see less and less student dependency on the words of the frames. Rather than confining students, the frames encourage them to branch out and to develop and present ideas in their own way.

This workbook is divided into four sections, with each section equivalent to ten weeks of work. At the end of each quarter, you will find an evaluation tool which the student should complete and return to you. Teachers who prefer to use the frames on an irregular basis should use the material at the beginning of the workbook first, as the frames do increase in difficulty.

During the first quarter of work, each page contains a writing frame with specific instructions and writing suggestions. The student is asked to fill in the paragraphs with appropriate words and is encouraged to rearrange words or delete words. It is crucial to the success of the program that each student use the writing frames as rough-draft pages and recopy their paragraphs on the lined workbook pages, using margins and legible penmanship.

During the second quarter the concept of *webbing* is introduced. A web is a series of linked balloons, with each balloon equivalent to an entry in an outline. Through a web, the student is encouraged to expand ideas.

By the end of the year students should realize that writing is a process which begins with brainstorming and moves through writing, revising, editing, and preparing the final draft. The writer is a craftsman who learns his craft by writing; these frames offer all students an opportunity to become writers.

First Quarter
Writing Frames

Frame 1

A writing frame is a partially completed paragraph which offers you writing ideas. Read the frame as it is written. Fill in the blanks with appropriate words. Don't hesitate to rearrange words if you wish. When you are finished and have carefully checked your work, rewrite your frame on the following lined page. Remember to leave margins and write clearly. Don't forget your title and be sure to write the date under your name in the upper right-hand corner of your final copy. This first frame will be about using writing frames. Good luck.

Using Frames

Writing is not always ....

.... Sometimes it is hard to get a good idea. Today

my teacher, ... ,

talked about writing frames and gave me a writing assignment using a

.... This frame, and

the others I will be assigned, will give me writing ideas. If I want to change

.... or ....

.... I may do so. When I finish filling in

the .... , I am to recopy

my paragraph on .... in my

best .... I must remember

to date my work. When my recopied work is finished I will ....

....

Date ....

Using Frames

....
....
....
....
....
....
....
....
....
....
....
....
....
....
....
....
....
....
....
....

Frame 2

In this writing frame you will be discussing the most popular school day of the week: Friday. Read the paragraph before filling in the blanks. If you wish to rearrange words, do so. Remember, you may add or delete anything you wish. Perhaps you can think of a more interesting way to end the paragraph. When you have finished, recopy your work on the following page. Write your name in the upper right-hand corner of your paper and place the date under it. Write clearly and leave margins.

Fridays

Friday is a day I ....

because I know the weekend is ....

.... When I wake up on Friday

morning I .... there

is only one more day, and that makes ....

.... Another reason

Friday is fun is that the teachers seem ....

.... and everyone

is ....

When the bell rings at the end of the school day, everyone

.... , for

they know ....

Fridays are ....

       Writing Frames

Date . . . .

Fridays

. . . .

. . . .

. . . .

. . . .

. . . .

. . . .

. . . .

. . . .

. . . .

. . . .

. . . .

. . . .

. . . .

. . . .

. . . .

. . . .

. . . .

. . . .

. . . .

Writing Frames

Frame 3

In this writing frame you will be asked to write about watching television. Read the paragraph before filling in the blanks; this will give you time to do some thinking about the subject before you complete the paragraph. The work you do on this sheet is your first draft. You may rearrange sentences and add words. Or, you may delete words. When you have finished, recopy your work on the following page, which is to be your final draft. This copy should be carefully done. Don't forget your name, the date, the title, and margins.

Television

I spend about .... hours a

.... watching television. I enjoy it

because .... I have

.... favorite shows. Each of them is

.... If I could watch

only one, I would watch ....

This is my favorite show because of ...., who

is my favorite character. Each week ....

.... gets into ....

because .... The problem

is usually solved when ....

If you like ...., watch

....

Writing Frames

Date ....

Television

....

....

....

....

....

....

....

....

....

....

....

....

....

....

....

....

....

....

....

....

....

Date ....

Frame 4

In this writing frame you will be writing about something you enjoy doing. The frame will help you to figure out why you selected this activity. Read the paragraph over carefully before beginning to fill in the blanks. Change any word or groups of words to fit your writing needs. When you have finished, recopy your work in final-draft form on the following page, using margins and including a title. Don't forget to write your name and the date in the upper right-hand corner.

My Favorite Activity

Reading, swimming, biking, and watching television are among the

things people enjoy doing in their spare time. When I was younger, I spent

a lot of time .... ;

but now that I am older I find that ....

.... Some of my friends like to

...., but when I have some

time to myself I usually ....

.... This may not sound exciting

to some people, but I enjoy it because ....

.... The only thing I

need to .... is

.... It's more fun when the weather

is .... , because

if it rains it ....

Date . . . .

My Favorite Activity

. . . .

. . . .

. . . .

. . . .

. . . .

. . . .

. . . .

. . . .

. . . .

. . . .

. . . .

. . . .

. . . .

. . . .

. . . .

. . . .

. . . .

. . . .

. . . .

Frame 5

In this writing frame you will be writing about a family tradition. Most families have traditions which may vary from having a special cake for birthdays to always eating baked beans on Saturday night. Read the following paragraphs carefully before filling in the blanks. You may change the words in the paragraph if you wish. When you are satisfied with this rough draft, rewrite your words neatly on the lined page. Be sure to write your name and the date in the upper right-hand corner and your title a few lines below. Choose your own title if you wish. Good luck.

A Family Tradition

The dictionary says that a tradition is a belief or . . . .

. . . . which is . . . .

For example, in some families it is a tradition to . . . .

. . . . stockings on Christmas Eve or eat

. . . . on Thanksgiving.

My family has . . . . traditions.

One I especially like is . . . . On

. . . . we get together to

. . . . I think the

tradition started when . . . .

. . . . Traditions are important because . . . .

. . . .

Date ....

A Family Tradition

....

....

....

....

....

....

....

....

....

....

....

....

....

....

....

....

....

....

....

....

Frame 6

Before you begin this writing frame, think about the people you know who seem to understand you. As you read the paragraphs, think about the person who would best fit the description given in the frame and then fill in the blanks and rearrange the words as you wish. When you are satisfied with your work, rewrite this paragraph on the following lined page in your best handwriting. Remember to write your name, the date, and a title. Good luck.

Someone Who Understands

We all need someone to understand us. Some people turn to their .... or their ....
when they need help. I always talk to ....
because I know that .... ,
who is my .... , really understands
me. We've known each other for ....
We first met when .... At
first we .... , but after a while
I learned that .... was a
person I could trust and one who would always ....
.... me.

We have had a lot of fun together. I'll never forget the time we
.... I guess people
understand each other best when ....
....

Date ....

Someone Who Understands

....

....

....

....

....

....

....

....

....

....

....

....

....

....

....

....

....

....

....

....

....

....

....

Frame 7

Everyone has bad dreams once in a while. Do you remember one you have had? Remember how your body felt as you awoke from it? Do you remember the prickly feeling in your legs? What else do you remember? In this frame try to think of words that will show how you felt. Read the frame carefully and then fill in the blanks. Be sure to add sentences to the frame to make it more interesting. When you are finished, recopy your work in final-draft form on the following page with name, date, and title. Good luck.

A Dream

One night I woke up so scared I . . . . I had been dreaming that . . . . and that I was . . . . When I woke up my heart was . . . . and my face felt . . . .

My legs felt . . . . I was so afraid I didn't dare . . . . The dream seemed so real that I . . . .

I can't imagine what caused this dream. Perhaps it was because I had been watching . . . . on television. Maybe it was because I had eaten . . . . just before going to bed.

Date ....

A Dream

....
....
....
....
....
....
....
....
....
....
....
....
....
....
....
....
....
....
....
....
....

Date . . . .

Frame 8

Everyone has a favorite month of the year. What's yours? Is it July when school is out? Is it the month in which you were born? As you fill in this writing frame, try to use words that will help your reader "see" what you see. Within the frame, words are suggested that you might want to use. You decide what is right for you. Read the frame before filling in any of the words. When you have done the best job possible, recopy your work in final-draft form on the following page.

My Favorite Month

My favorite month of the year is . . . .

because a great deal happens in . . . . The weather

is . . . . (hot, cool, beautiful, clear) and

. . . . (comfortable, refreshing, cold, snowy) so I can

. . . . Lakes and streams

are . . . . , which makes it possible

for me to . . . . In

addition to this, ... is in . . . . ,

and I enjoy . . . . and . . . .

During this month my family usually . . . .

I look forward to this month every year.

Date ....

My Favorite Month

....

....

....

....

....

....

....

....

....

....

....

....

....

....

....

....

....

....

....

....

Frame 9

It's always a good idea to look back. This frame gives you an opportunity to look back to the first day of school. Were you nervous? Were you anxious to get it over with? Read the frame carefully before filling in the blanks. Remember that you may not want to use all the sentences given. That's fine. Use what works for you. When you are satisfied with your work, recopy the frame in final-draft form.

The First Day

Probably the hardest part of getting back to school is the first day. I

remember this . . . . that the day

before school started I was . . . . All my

friends felt the same way. . . . . said he

didn't care if . . . . , but . . . .

didn't agree. . . . . said that school was

. . . . I just . . . . it. I

found it . . . . to sleep the night before, and

when the alarm went off I . . . .

Once I got to school and began seeing . . . .

it wasn't so bad. I was even glad to see . . . .

Once classes started, though, I felt . . . .

and decided to . . . . That first

day was . . . .

Date ....

The First Day

....

....

....

....

....

....

....

....

....

....

....

....

....

....

....

....

....

....

....

....

Frame 10

We all make mistakes. In this frame you are asked to think about one of your mistakes and what, if anything, you learned from making the mistake.

Fill in the frame as you always do. Don't move on to making a copy of your frame until another person has read your work. Ask that person to say one good thing about your frame and make one suggestion to improve it. When you have made your changes, write your final draft.

My Mistake

The day on which I made my biggest mistake started ....

.... At that time I didn't .... If

I had, I .... It's too late to

do anything about it now, but I ....

My problems began when ....

At first I .... , but soon realized

that .... It was then that

I began to .... , but ....

.... Now, when I look back, I realize I ....

.... But I didn't think of that then.

Did I learn anything from making this mistake? That's a good question,

one I can answer by saying ....

....

Date . . . .

My Mistake

. . . .

. . . .

. . . .

. . . .

. . . .

. . . .

. . . .

. . . .

. . . .

. . . .

. . . .

. . . .

. . . .

. . . .

. . . .

. . . .

. . . .

. . . .

. . . .

. . . .

FIRST QUARTER EVALUATION

Congratulations! You have completed one fourth of the frames in this workbook. If these frames are to aid you in becoming a better writer, it is important for you to evaluate your progress. Read the following statements carefully and follow the directions. As you complete each numbered set of directions, place a check mark in front of the number. Each check is worth 10 points, for a total of 100. When you finish with the evaluation, total the points for your grade.

1. Look back over your rewritten paragraphs, starting with Frame 1 and ending with Frame 10.

2. Read your first frame. Select one sentence from the paragraph that you think can be improved by adding new words. Rewrite the sentence on the lines below.

   . . . .

   . . . .

3. Check your second frame for incorrectly spelled words. Cross out any errors and write the words correctly.

4. Look for capitalization errors in your third frame. Be sure you capitalized the important words in the title of the television show you wrote about.

First Quarter Evaluation

5. Read through your next three frames to see if you have overused the word *and.* If you have used it more than two or three times per paragraph, try combining your ideas in different ways. You may find that the *and's* can be replaced by periods, or that another word is more effective.

6. Read through the next three frames and select your favorite. Which did you choose? ....

7. Why did you select this paragraph? ....

    ....

8. Read your last frame looking for descriptive words. Underline any words you particularly like.

9. Now that you have read through all your finished pieces, write a sentence in which you say something good about your writing.

    ....

    ....

    ....

10. State one way in which you could improve your writing.

    ....

    ....

TOTAL YOUR POINTS. If you did not complete a set of directions, you receive no credit for work partially done. Write your grade here. ....

Second Quarter
Writing Frames

Frame 11

In an earlier frame, you had to think back to the first day of school this year. In this frame, you are asked to remember your thoughts and feelings at that time, then compare them to your attitude towards school today. Read the paragraph carefully before adding or changing any words. Try to use specific words which show exactly how you felt then and how you feel now. Write your work in final-draft form. This means to write it neatly on the lined page, remembering to include the date.

First Impressions

Now that we have been in school for .... ,

I feel .... about my classes and teachers.

At first, ... seemed interesting,

but now .... My hardest class is

.... because ....

My teacher in that class, ..., usually

.... , which is .... for me.

My easiest class is .... , which I have with

.... The work is easy because ....

I have learned .... this fall. For

example, I now know that .... Grades

are coming out soon. I hope that ....

Date ....

First Impressions

....
....
....
....
....
....
....
....
....
....
....
....
....
....
....
....
....
....
....
....

27   *Writing Frames*

Frame 12

You probably would agree that being young isn't always fun or easy. Some older people think back to their school days as the best days of their lives. They seem to have forgotten the difficult times. In this frame you will have an opportunity to write about the problems people your age have. Read the paragraph before beginning to write. Notice that you need to add your age to the title. Good luck.

The Trials and Tribulations of Being . . . .

One of the expressions I dislike the most is, "Now is the best time of your

life." Every time I turn around my . . . .

or . . . . says something like that to me. I guess

they . . . . what being a . . . . is. When they

think of being young, they think of . . . .

and . . . . They forget about . . . . ,

. . . . , and . . . . I wonder how

they would like it if they suddenly found themselves . . . . years old

again. How would they like having to ask for everything from

. . . . to . . . . ? If older

people had to be young for one day, perhaps they . . . .

. . . .

Date ....

The Trials and Tribulations of Being ....

....

....

....

....

....

....

....

....

....

....

....

....

....

....

....

....

....

....

....

....

....

Frame 13

The connected balloons in the middle of this page are called a *web*. The purpose of a web is to help you think of writing ideas. Notice that the big center balloon has the words "a good friend." From this balloon you will see smaller connecting balloons with words which describe a friend. If you can think of other words to describe a friend, add words of your own. Use the words from the web to fill in your writing frame.

Remember to recopy your paragraph when you are finished.

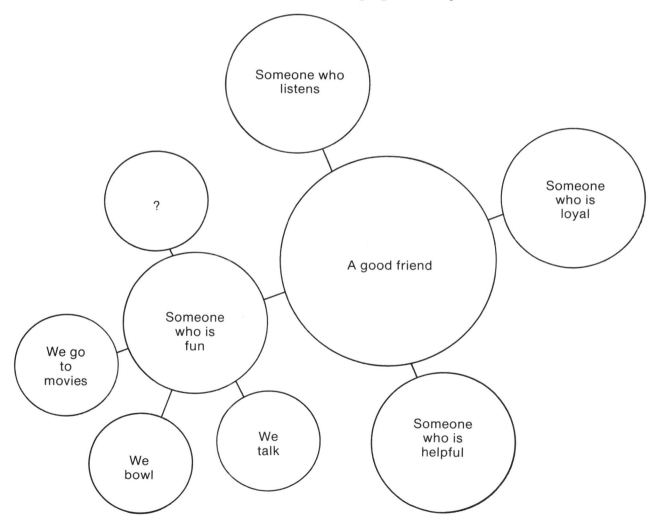

Date ....

A Friend

A friend is someone who ....

....

and is always .... When

someone needs .... it is

important to .... A good

friend never ....

.... ,

He/she has time to ....

....

A friend isn't just someone who helps in times of trouble, though. A

friend is also someone to ....

.... ,

Friends usually spend .... together

talking, ... ,

.... , and ....

Everything is more .... with

a ....

A Friend

. . . .

. . . .

. . . .

. . . .

. . . .

. . . .

. . . .

. . . .

. . . .

. . . .

. . . .

. . . .

. . . .

. . . .

. . . .

. . . .

. . . .

. . . .

Frame 14

In the last frame you wrote about friends. You did not have an opportunity to write about a special friend. This web and frame will give you a chance to do that. The web has been started for you. Write your friend's name in the center balloon. In the balloons around it, write the information asked for. Add as many balloons and words as you can. When you are finished, fill in the frame, which becomes your rough draft. Reread this draft before rewriting it in your best handwriting. If possible, ask someone close by to read your work.

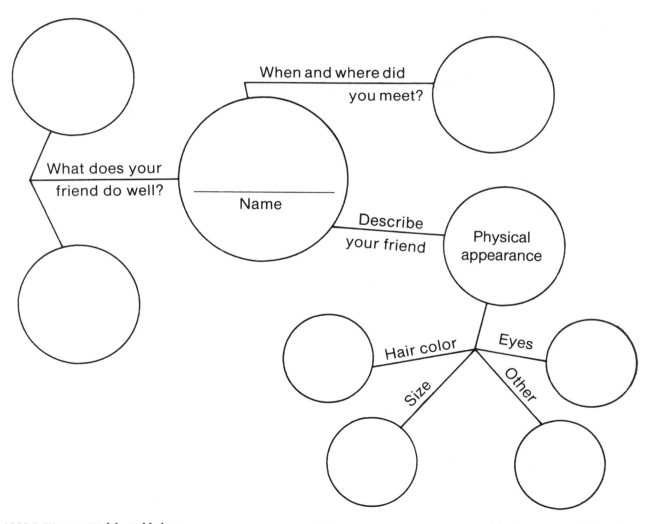

Date ....

A Good Friend

.... is one of my best friends. We first

met .... years ago when ....

I thought at that time that ....

....

.... is about .... feet tall with

.... eyes and ....

hair, which is always .... I think my friend is

....

We do a lot of things together. We like to ....

.... Sometimes we

.... No

matter what we do, we always ....

.... A good

friend is ....

Date ....

A Good Friend

....
....
....
....
....
....
....
....
....
....
....
....
....
....
....
....
....
....
....
....
....

Frame 15

Think back to last Thanksgiving. Where were you? Who were you with? What did you eat for your Thanksgiving dinner? Was it turkey, or did your family decide to be different and eat pizza? Study the web below and add specific words in the empty balloons to describe last Thanksgiving. Notice in this web that many of the larger balloons have smaller balloons attached. These smaller balloons are for additional words which help to make your reader "see" what you are describing. The completed balloons should give you the idea. When you have finished the web, move on to the frame. If possible, read your completed frame to a friend, or ask a friend to read your completed frame and make any suggestions which will make it better. Your last step in completing this assignment is to write and date your final draft.

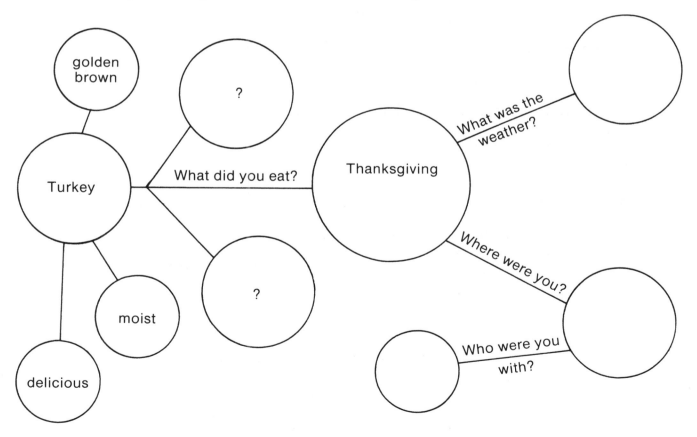

Date ....

A Thanksgiving Memory

I spent last Thanksgiving with ....

.... It was a .... day.

The sky was .... and

the ....

We decided to .... the

weather and celebrate Thanksgiving by ....

Everyone was .... and ....

to the big day.

Last year my family decided to have ....

.... for dinner.

With it we had .... ,

.... , ... , and

.... The ....

and the .... made

the table look very ....

Everything was .... , but I

especially enjoyed the ....

I .... Thanksgiving.

         Writing Frames

Date ....

A Thanksgiving Memory

....

....

....

....

....

....

....

....

....

....

....

....

....

....

....

....

....

....

....

....

....

Frame 16

Our calendar is filled with a variety of holidays. Which is your favorite? Why? How do you get ready for it? How do you celebrate?

Fill in the balloons in the web below before beginning work on your frame. Concentrate on using colorful and action-packed words. Use the name of your favorite holiday as the title of the frame. Remember, you may change words or sentences in the frame to meet your writing needs. When your frame is finished, read it to a friend or ask a friend to read it and make suggestions.

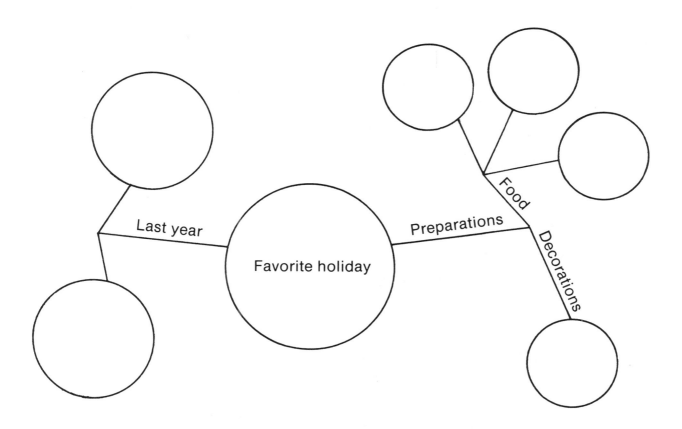

Date ....

....

I begin thinking about getting ready for ....

in .... when ....

I always plan to ....

but never .... When

.... says, " ....

.... ,"

I know .... is close.

My family and friends prepare for the day by ....

....

We usually enjoy special foods, including ....

.... , ... , and

....

Last year when ....

arrived I .... This

year I hope ....

44

Date ....

....

....

....

....

....

....

....

....

....

....

....

....

....

....

....

....

....

....

....

....

....

....

Frame 17

As we move closer to the beginning of a new year, it is helpful to look back at the past year. In this frame you will have an opportunity to write about what you have done this year. Begin by filling in the balloons in your web. Remember, you may add balloons or leave them out. Make the web *your* web. When you are satisfied, complete the frame. Ask another student to read your frame and offer suggestions to make it better. When you have done all that you can do, copy your frame on the following page.

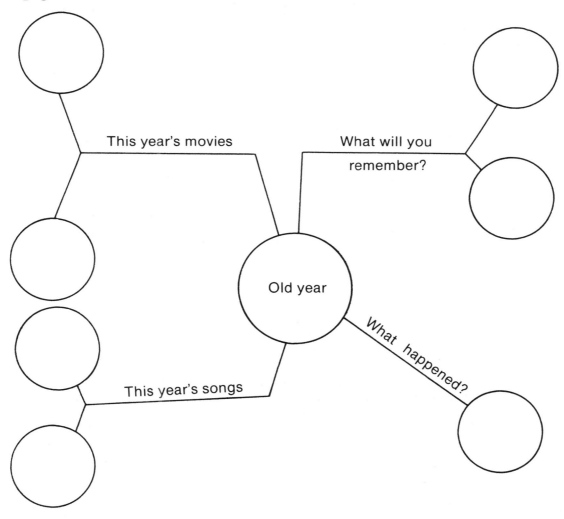

Date . . . .

The Old Year

This year has been . . . .
for me. When it started last January, I was . . . .

. . . .

What I will remember about this year is . . . . ,
which happened in . . . .
I will also remember . . . .
because . . . .
I'll never forget . . . .
and how . . . . I was

. . . .

I can't remember a lot of what happened in the world this year, but I do
remember . . . .
and . . . .
There is so much news that it is hard to remember very much.

My favorite movie this year was . . . .
. . . . If I had
to pick my favorite song I would . . . .
. . . . I wonder what I will be
writing at this time next year.

   Writing Frames

Date ....

The Old Year

Frame 18

In your last frame you wrote about the old year. In this frame you will write about the new year. Begin by filling in the balloons in your web. Remember, you may add balloons or leave them out. When you are finished with your web, complete the frame. Ask someone nearby to read your completed work. If you both are satisfied that you have done your best, recopy the frame as a final draft. Don't forget to date your final draft.

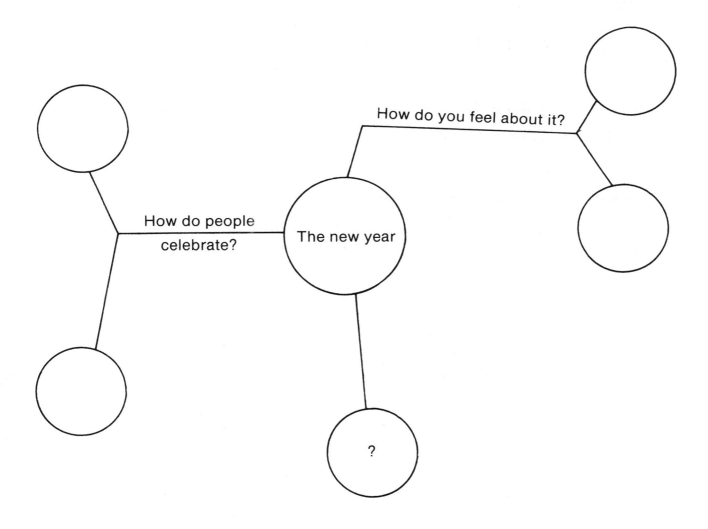

Date ....

The New Year

I am ....

.... the new year because I ....

.... Everyone around me is talking about ....

.... Some people say they ....

.... while others say ....

Personally, I think ....

I wonder what the new year will bring. I am sure that ....

.... and that I will ....

Other than that, I'm not sure ....

It's interesting to watch people get ready for the new year. Some ....

.... and then .... ,

The best way to get ready for a new year is ....

.... , and that's what I am going to do.

Date ....

The New Year

....

....

....

....

....

....

....

....

....

....

....

....

....

....

....

....

....

....

....

Date ....

Frame 19

What have you learned this year in school? What do you remember learning in social studies? How about math? What have you been doing in science and English? In this frame you will have an opportunity to show what you have learned. Think back and write. If you want to do a web, draw your own on another sheet of paper and then fill in your frame. If you prefer to work without a web, do so.

When your frame is complete, read it out loud to someone. If it sounds smooth, you are ready to copy your work. If your frame is difficult to read, try to make it smoother by changing words. When you are satisified, make your final copy.

What I Am Learning

This year I am taking .... subjects. My subjects are .... ,

.... , ... , ... , and ....

My favorite subject is .... , where I have learned ....

.... , ... , and .... I am

never going to forget .... , which my teacher, ... ,

taught us last .... The hardest subject I am taking is

.... In that class right now we are studying .... and

.... , which I find .... Nothing is easy for me in that class.

The easiest subject I am taking is .... , which is taught by

.... (who is ....). We have

learned .... in that class this year. What I remember best is

.... I remember that because ....

Now that I think about it, I've learned ....

Date ....

What I Am Learning

....

....

....

....

....

....

....

....

....

....

....

....

....

....

....

....

....

....

....

....

....

Frame 20

You are going to take a "word snapshot." Look around your classroom and select a person to "photograph." What is interesting about this person—hair, clothing, features? Study the person's expression. Is this a happy, sad, or excited face that you see? When this person works, does he/she chew on a pencil or tap a foot? Think about the impressions this person's appearance makes.

When you are ready to begin, fill in the frame below, using the person's name in the first slot. If you wish, you may do a web on another sheet. Notice that there is a long slot at the end of the paragraph for you to add a sentence of your own. Try to think of an ending which finishes the snapshot and helps your reader to "see" your photograph.

Take the time to reread your rough draft (the frame) or ask someone else to check it before you write your final draft.

A Snapshot

. . . . 's eyes are . . . . , ...

His/Her hair is . . . . and cut in . . . . You can

tell that . . . . jewelry because . . . .

. . . . is about . . . . feet tall but looks . . . .

because . . . .

Usually . . . . wears . . . . or

. . . . Today he/she is wearing . . . .

with a . . . . and . . . . ,

He/She looks . . . .

When . . . . works he/she always . . . . ,

which means . . . . 's favorite expression is

. . . . , which he/she says all the time.

. . . .

. . . .

Date ....

A Snapshot

....

....

....

....

....

....

....

....

....

....

....

....

....

....

....

....

....

....

....

Date ....

SECOND QUARTER EVALUATION

Congratulations! You have completed one half of the frame sheets in this writing series. It is now time to read over the work you have completed during the last ten weeks. Do that before you begin filling in the questions below.

As you complete each numbered set of questions, place a check mark in front of the number. Each of the first 8 checks is worth 10 points. Number 9 is worth 5 points, and number 10 is worth 15 points. When you finish with the evaluation, total the points for your grade.

1. Read your first frame for this quarter. Write the words from that frame which describe how you feel about school.

   ....

   ....

2. Read your second frame. Write a sentence in which you explain why you enjoyed or didn't enjoy completing this frame.

   ....

   ....

3. Did the web help you get ready for Frame 13? .... Why or why not?

   ....

   ....

4. Reread Frame 14. What do you think is most important to you in a friend? ....

   ....

   ....

Second Quarter Evaluation

5. Reread your fifth frame for this quarter. On the line which follows, write the words which you used in the frame to describe what you ate on Thanksgiving.

   . . . .

   . . . .

6. Check for capitalization errors in your sixth frame. Did you remember to capitalize the name of your special holiday every time you wrote it? On the line which follows, correctly write any words you forgot to capitalize.

   . . . .

7. Select your favorite sentence from Frame 17. Write it on the following lines.

   . . . .

   . . . .

8. Which was your favorite frame? Why? . . . .

   . . . .

   . . . .

9. On the following line, write the title of the frame which you think you can improve by adding new words or sentences.

   . . . .

10. Rewrite and improve the frame you listed in Question 9. Attach your old copy and the rewritten copy to this evaluation.

Third Quarter
Writing Frames

Frame 21

Each of us has met someone during our lifetime whom we admire. It may be someone we have known personally, or someone we have read about. Who is the person you most admire? Is it a relative who is always willing to help others? Is it a national leader who has done great things for our country? Is it a great sports hero who has beaten the odds? Make a list of people you admire. Then select one person to write about.

Read the frame carefully before you start writing. Notice that there is an empty sentence slot at the end of the last paragraph. Try to think of a strong ending for your work.

When you are finished, ask another person in your class to read over what you have written. Ask them for suggestions which will improve your work. When you are satisfied with what you have done, copy your frame on the following page.

A Person I Admire

.... is a person I admire because ....

.... I first heard about .... when I was

.... At first I wasn't very impressed, but when I learned

.... , I decided that this

was a very special person.

.... is best known for .... ,

which happened .... years ago. At that time he/she was ....

.... Since that time, he/she has .... , which has

....

Why has .... been so successful? I think it is because he/she

....

....

Date ....

A Person I Admire

....

....

....

....

....

....

....

....

....

....

....

....

....

....

....

....

....

....

....

....

....

....

Frame 22

As you know, writing webs are designed to help you to write. The webs you have had so far this year have been partially completed, but there will be a time when it will be your job to fill in all the balloons in a writing web. You should think of a writing web as a warm-up exercise intended to get you ready to write. When you fill in a web, try to add as many words and ideas as you can. You don't have to use all the words, but they are there if you need them.

Notice that the web on the next page is in the middle of the frame. Read over the frame carefully before completing it. As always, ask another person to check your work before you write the frame in final-draft form. Be sure to copy over the web in your final draft.

Date ....

Writing Webs

The first time I saw a writing web I thought ....
.... I didn't think a web would ....
For those of you who don't know what a writing web is, let me explain.
A web is .... A writer who is trying
to get .... fills in ....
with words which ....

A writer writing about his or her favorite animal would write the words
"my .... " in the big center balloon. From the
big center balloon, the writer would draw smaller balloons, and in each balloon
he would write a word which tells more about that favorite animal. As the
writer gets more ideas, he or she would keep adding balloons. For example:

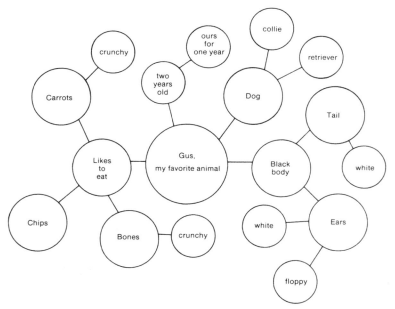

For those of you who haven't tried writing webs, I say ....
.... I have found them ....

                                                           Writing Frames

Writing Webs

....

....

....

....

....

....

....

....

....

....

....

....

....

....

....

....

....

....

....

....

Frame 23

Let's continue with the subject of favorite animals. In the web below there is a central balloon for the subject of the composition. (Don't let the word *composition* worry you; it just means a well-planned piece of writing.) Attached to the balloon is a series of lines which lead to smaller balloons and more lines and balloons.

Study the web for a minute. Notice that one set of balloons describes Spot's size. Another set of balloons describes Spot. The last set of balloons tells what Spot enjoys doing. The writer could add another set of balloons which would show why Spot is his or her favorite animal. Once a writer has finished a web, he or she is ready to write an interesting paragraph with lots of specific detail.

After studying the web, go on to the frame. Fill in the slots and then ask someone in your class to check your work. When you are satisfied, copy it in final-draft form.

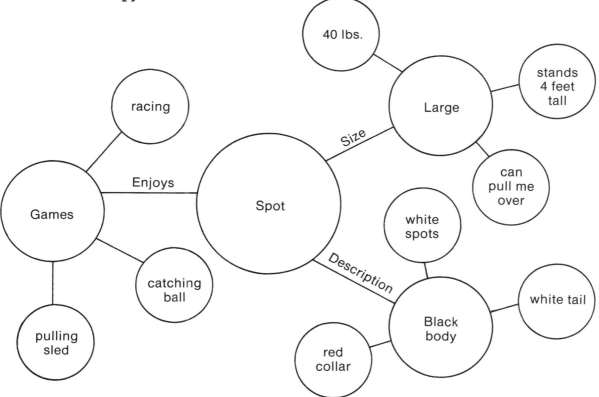

Writing Webs II

If you look at the web about Spot, you will notice that the writer has information for .... paragraphs. One paragraph would be about .... The second paragraph would be about .... , and the third paragraph would be about .... In other words, each set .... becomes a ....

If the writer wanted to add a fourth .... , he would draw another set of balloons and add specific information about that topic. Some of the topics the writer could add are .... , ... , or ....

A writing web helps .... because .... ,

Writing Frames

Date ....

Writing Webs II

....

....

....

....

....

....

....

....

....

....

....

....

....

....

....

....

....

....

....

....

....

Frame 24

In this frame you will be writing about your favorite place. Where do you want to be when you are either very happy or very sad? Is there a room in your home where you always feel comfortable, or do you have a place in the woods or in a park? Fill in the writing web below. Try to add new topic balloons to this web. When you have finished, fill in the frame, have another person read it, and write the final draft. Have you noticed that the steps to a final draft are always the same?

because

Location

color

Makes me feel

My favorite place

_____

because

I found it?

how?

when?

Date ....

My Favorite Place

When I am .... or ....

I like to go to my .... , which is ....

It's a .... with ....

.... ,

When I am there I always ....

.... ,

I first found this spot when ....

.... I had been ....

.... when suddenly I ....

From that time on I have .... , ...

knows I go there. ....

....

.... ,

Date ....

My Favorite Place

....
....
....
....
....
....
....
....
....
....
....
....
....
....
....
....
....
....
....
....
....

Writing Frames

Frame 25

What is your favorite kind of day? Is it a sunny Saturday when you have a chance to be outside? Is it a snowy winter day when school has been called off because of storms? Or, is it a birthday or some type of anniversary? Follow the steps you have followed all year to complete this assignment.

1. Fill in the web.
2. Complete the frame.
3. Ask someone to read your work.
4. Write your final draft.

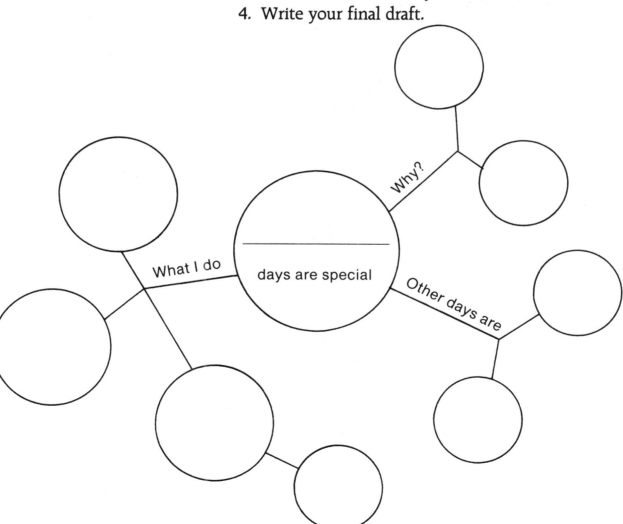

Date ....

.... Days Are Special

.... special. I always look

forward to .... because I know ....

.... I begin thinking about .... when

.... It is difficult to explain why I get excited

about .... , but I guess it is because ....

When you think about it, most days are .... ,

which makes them ....

When a .... arrives I begin the day by

.... Later on in the morning I

.... My afternoon is spent ....

.... When mealtime arrives I like to have

.... , which is one of my favorites. I top off

my special day by ....

                                       Writing Frames

Date ....

.... Days Are Special

....

....

....

....

....

....

....

....

....

....

....

....

....

....

....

....

....

....

....

....

....

Frame 26

If you could go anywhere you wanted to for vacation, where would you go? What would you do? This web and frame give you a chance to describe your dream vacation.

Study the web and write in as many ideas as possible. Then fill in the frame. Remember that you may make changes in the frame if you wish. When the frame is complete, go through the steps you have followed in previous writing assignments.

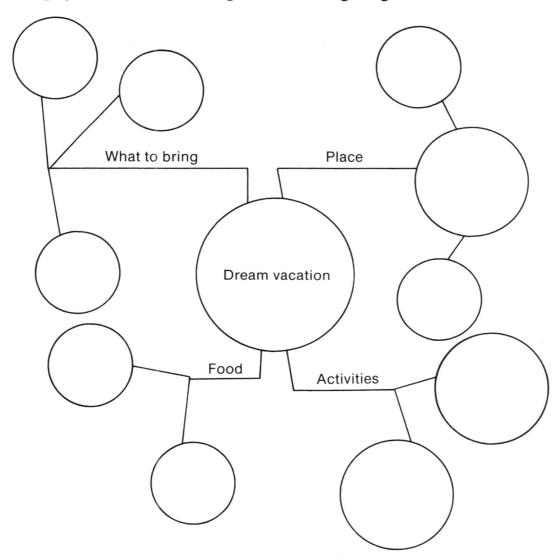

Date ....

My Dream Vacation

To me, the most .... place to go on vacation

would be .... I'd like to spend

.... there. I'd go by .... , my favorite way

to travel. I'd need to bring ....

with me and some .... The climate

is .... , so I'd need .... and

.... Of course, I'd buy new clothes for the trip!

The first thing I'd do is ....

I hear the .... is excellent there. I'd

also leave some time for ....

Trying local foods is one of the best parts of traveling. I would try

.... , ... , and

.... while I was there. Maybe I'd pick up some ....

.... to bring home. I'd also buy colorful postcards to send to

.... back home.

This is all imagined, of course. But I can dream, can't I?

Writing Frames

Date ....

My Dream Vacation

....
....
....
....
....
....
....
....
....
....
....
....
....
....
....
....
....
....
....
....
....
....

Frame 27

In this writing frame you'll get to use your imagination. Fill in the web below and add any other information you wish. When your web is finished, complete the frame. Ask another student to read it and give you his or her comments. Recopy the frame in final-draft form.

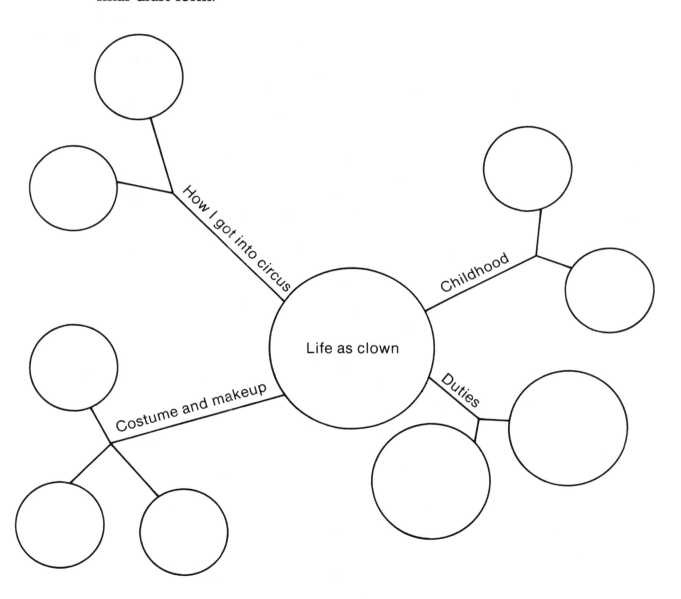

Date ....

My Life as a Circus Clown

I wasn't born a circus clown, you know. When I was small my family lived

in .... Life in .... was

.... It was when the circus visited when I was 10 that I decided

.... When I was ...... I got my chance.

Here's how it happened: ....

....

Now I make regular appearances with the .... Circus.

My day begins early. I put on my costume, which includes ....

.... Then I do

my face and wig, which .... Although I

make people laugh, it's a hard life. Few people realize that performers also have

off-stage duties, such as .... and ....

In between shows I also make up new ideas to add to my act. I think I'll add

....

After .... shows a day, I'm a pretty tired clown. But seeing all

those happy kids makes me feel .... It's

worth all the hard work to see people laughing.

Date ....

My Life as a Circus Clown

....

....

....

....

....

....

....

....

....

....

....

....

....

....

....

....

....

....

....

....

Frame 28

Can you remember a story told to you by an older person about school before the days of calculators and computers, about traveling before the age of airplanes, or about buying food before the days of supermarkets or malls? In this assignment you are asked to retell such a story. It is through these kinds of stories that local or family history is preserved. If you can't remember any stories about the "old days," you might want to discuss the topic with an older person before beginning the web and frame.

You will notice that there are many empty slots in the frame. If you do your web carefully, you should have no trouble with the frame. Remember, you don't have to use all the words or slots. Complete the assignment as you have the other frames in this series.

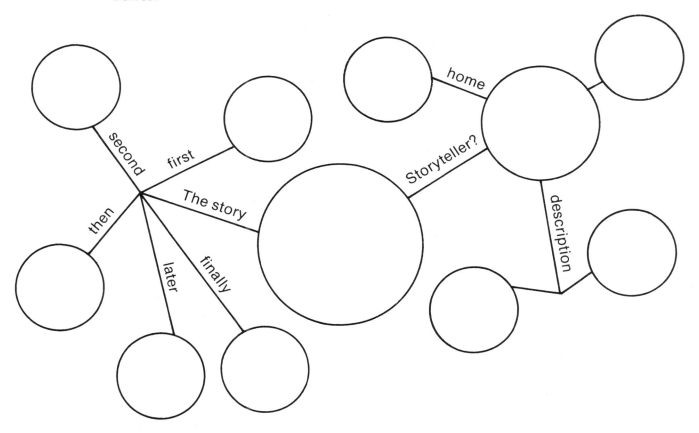

Date ....

....

.... , who told me this story, is

.... ,

.... lives in .... in

a .... I spend ....

time with .... whenever ....

Here's what .... told me: .... years ago when

.... ,

.... It seems

that .... ,

but .... It was about

.... later that ....

....

....

.... ,

I like this story because ....

....

.... ,

Date ....

....

....

....

....

....

....

....

....

....

....

....

....

....

....

....

....

....

....

....

....

....

....

....

Frame 29

No matter what kind of music you like, just about everyone loves to go to concerts. The special thrill of being in a big, happy crowd, the hush when the lights go down . . . It's a magic time. In this web you are asked to recall a concert you have attended.

Fill in the web and frame as you always do. Don't move on to making a copy of your frame until another person has read your work. Ask that person to say one good thing about your frame and make one suggestion for improving it. When you have made your changes, write your final draft.

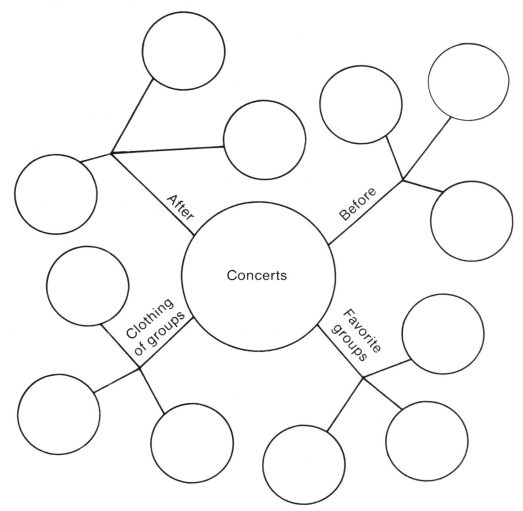

Date ....

A Special Concert

Concerts can be great .... I usually

like to go with my .... We usually meet

for dinner at .... and have ....

or .... We usually wear ....

Then we go to the .... and make our way to our seats.

After a while, the lights go down and the beginning of the concert is

announced. My favorite concert was by ....

.... They played ....

Their leader is really ....

.... wore ....

with .... the last time they were

here. You can bet the students at .... will be wearing

them soon, too! Afterwards, we went out to ....

for some .... Now to just recover until

.... comes to town!

Date ....

A Special Concert

....
....
....
....
....
....
....
....
....
....
....
....
....
....
....
....
....
....
....
....
....

Writing Frames

Frame 30

Do you have a favorite daydream? When you let your mind wander, do you dream about having an exciting, glamorous life, or do you daydream about being a famous scientist, writer, banker, or sports figure? In this web and frame you are going to write about your daydreams, so lean back and daydream. When ready, fill in the web and complete this assignment as you have all the others in this series.

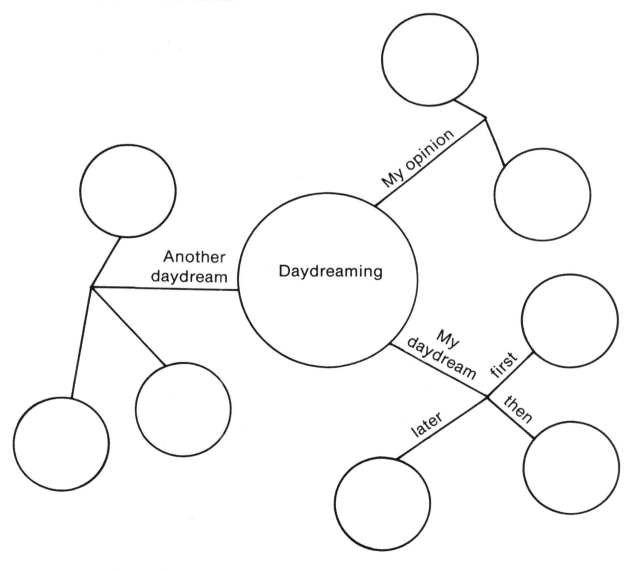

         Writing Frames

Date ....

Daydreams

Daydreaming is important because ....

I like to daydream when ....

Sometimes when I daydream I get ....

In my favorite daydream I ....

.... Then

....

.... Later on I ....

....

In another favorite daydream I .... ,

When that happens I ....

.... I don't understand

....

Some people say daydreaming is a waste of time. I think

....

....

Daydreams

....
....
....
....
....
....
....
....
....
....
....
....
....
....
....
....
....
....
....
....
....

Date . . . .

THIRD QUARTER EVALUATION

Congratulations! You have finished three quarters of the frames in this series. It is now time to read over the work you have completed during the last few weeks.

In this evaluation you will be asked to revise a number of sentences. To *revise* means to change a sentence by adding new words, taking out words, or rearranging the words already in place. There are fewer questions in this evaluation than in the others, because revising is difficult work.

As you complete each numbered question, place a check mark in front of the number. Each of the five questions is worth 20 points. In order to get any credit, you must finish all parts of a question. When you finish with the evaluation, total the points for your grade.

1. Read your first frame for this quarter. When you finish, revise both the first and last sentences. Write them on the lines below.

   . . . .

   . . . .

   . . . .

   . . . .

2. Rewrite "Writing Webs" in your own words on the lines below. Remember to include all the important ideas, and ask another student to reread your work to be sure it is clear.

   . . . .

   . . . .

   . . . .

Writing Frames

Date . . . .

Third Quarter Evaluation

. . . .

. . . .

3. Reread "My Favorite Place." Select one sentence you think you can improve, and write your revised sentence on the lines below.

. . . .

. . . .

4. Write a paragraph in which you explain the steps which you follow when you work with a web and frame.

. . . .

. . . .

. . . .

. . . .

. . . .

5. Select your favorite frame from those you have completed this quarter. On the lines below explain what it is you like about this frame.

. . . .

. . . .

. . . .

. . . .

Fourth Quarter
Writing Frames

Frame 31

We write best when we write about what we know. In this frame and the accompanying web you will be asked to think and write about things that you know. You might know quite a bit about cars, fashion, food, animals, or fishing.

Use as much of the web as you can before moving on to the frame. You will complete the frame as usual, ask another student to read it, rewrite it, and READ IT OVER TO BE SURE IT IS CORRECT. Notice that the words in all capitals state a new step to follow in completing a final draft.

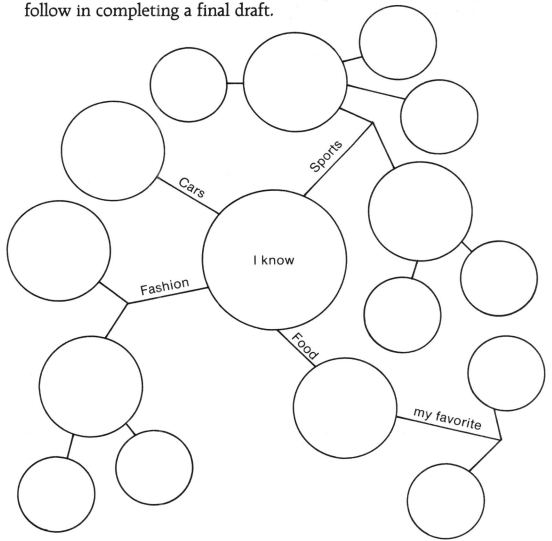

Writing Ideas

Among the outdoor things that interest me are .... ,
.... , and .... Of the three,
.... is my favorite and the one I know the most about.
In order to .... , you need a .... , a
.... , and a .... It is very
helpful to .... The perfect kind of weather
for this activity is ....
A .... day won't do.

When I am inside, I like to .... ,
.... , and .... Of those three activities,
I spend more of my time on .... than on the others.
.... is an activity best done when ....
.... I spend .... of time on this
activity because ....

Among other things I know and am interested in are .... ,
.... , ... , and
.... Some of my friends are interested in
.... , but I think ....
....

If I wrote about any of the activities mentioned in this composition I
would ....

Date ....

Writing Ideas

....

....

....

....

....

....

....

....

....

....

....

....

....

....

....

....

....

....

....

....

Frame 32

Words are a writer's tools, just as a hammer, nails, and wood are the tools of a carpenter. In each case, the craftsman will do a better job if he/she selects the correct tools for the job. When writing, writers too often are satisfied with their first word choice. This frame and accompanying web will encourage you to experiment with words whenever you write.

Complete the work as you have previous assignments in this workbook. Don't forget to read over your final draft!

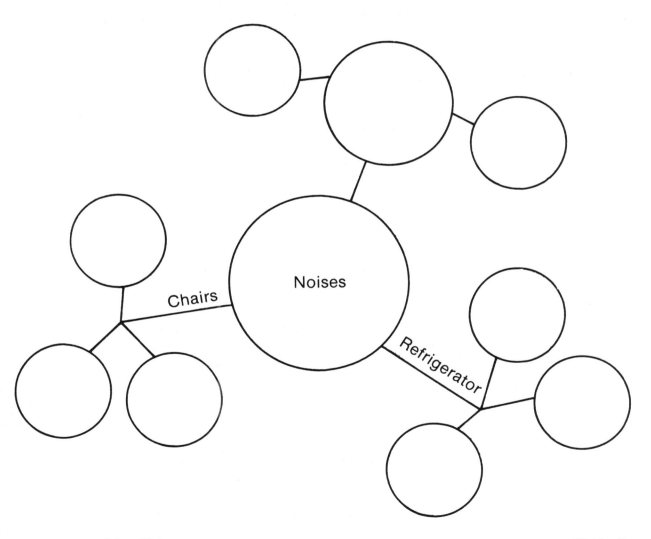

Date . . . .

Wondrous Words

Have you ever stopped to think about the number of sounds a refrigerator makes? When it is new it . . . . As it gets older it . . . . Whenever it is opened or closed it . . . . , ... , or . . . . I've even heard a refrigerator . . . .

Chairs are also very noisy. When a large person sits on them they . . . . Children make chairs . . . . , while dogs make them . . . . A rocking chair is the noisiest kind of chair, for it . . . . and . . . . whenever . . . .

The noisiest object in my house is . . . . , which . . . . and . . . . all the time. Whenever I . . . . I hear . . . . Sometimes I feel like . . . .

Some noises are bothersome, but many are . . . . Some of the noises I like are . . . . , ... , and . . . . The world certainly . . . .

Date ....

Wondrous Words

....

....

....

....

....

....

....

....

....

....

....

....

....

....

....

....

....

....

....

....

 Writing Frames

Frame 33

You rush to school each morning hoping you have remembered everything you need. Once in school, you have classes to attend, homework to complete, and friends to meet. Lunchtime is another rush, with everyone trying to get to the same place at the same time. In this frame and accompanying web you are asked to write about your school day. This is not meant to be a serious piece of writing; you are aiming for humor. Select your words carefully.

When you have finished the web and frame, continue to follow the writing steps you have used all year.

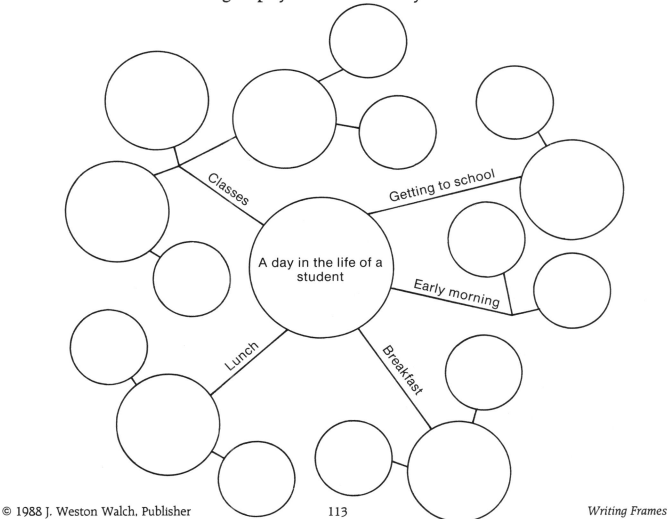

Date ....

One Day in the Life of a Student

My day begins when .... , which
means I must get up .... and ....
Breakfast is always .... for me. I
.... and then bolt out the door
to ....

The .... to school is the next thing I have
to face. It is always .... By the time I get to
school I am .... Things don't improve, because as soon
as I enter homeroom ....
From .... I .... to ....
where .... Until lunchtime I
.... , with never enough time to ....
....

I look forward to lunch because ....
....
.... Unfortunately, even lunchtime can get ....
.... when ....

When afternoon classes roll around I am ....
but .... It isn't easy being .... Finally,
school .... and it is time to ....

My evenings are spent ....
knowing full well that in a few short hours ....
....

Date ....

One Day in the Life of a Student

....

....

....

....

....

....

....

....

....

....

....

....

....

....

....

....

....

....

....

....

....

Frame 34

In the previous frame you had an opportunity to describe a day in the life of a student. Now it is time to do the same thing from a teacher's point of view. After all these years in school, you know quite a bit about teachers' outlooks and routines. As in the previous frame, your aim is humor. This is not meant to be a serious piece.

When you have finished the web and frame, continue to follow the writing steps you have used all year.

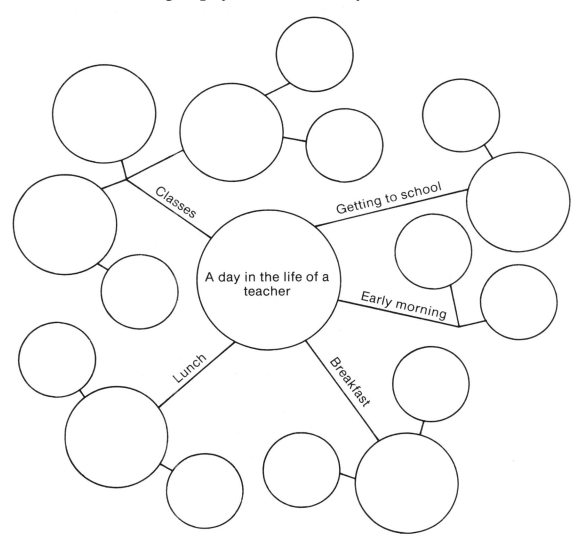

Date ....

One Day in the Life of a Teacher

My day begins when .... , which

means I must get up .... , ... ,

and .... For breakfast I always .... ,

which gives me the strength to face the day. The ....

to school is always .... , which puts me in a ....

.... mood before the school day even begins.

My first-period class is .... The students

in this class are .... and ....

Second-period class is .... , which is usually

.... By this time I could use a ....

but there isn't time. I'm off to ....

for another forty-five minutes of .... The rest

of the morning is spent .... , which means I am

.... when lunchtime comes.

I generally eat .... , which

means .... This is enough to ....

.... , but it is part of my job.

During the afternoon I .... and finish

off the day by .... I spend my evenings ....

.... Who said a teacher's life is .... ?

I think ....

118   *Writing Frames*

Date ....

One Day in the Life of a Teacher

....
....
....
....
....
....
....
....
....
....
....
....
....
....
....
....
....
....
....
....
....

Frame 35

You probably see a variety of fashions as you walk through your school. Each year, and sometimes each month, people are wearing something new. Take a look around you and then complete the following web and frame. Ask another student to check it over, and then write your final draft. Finish by rereading it to be sure it is the best you can do.

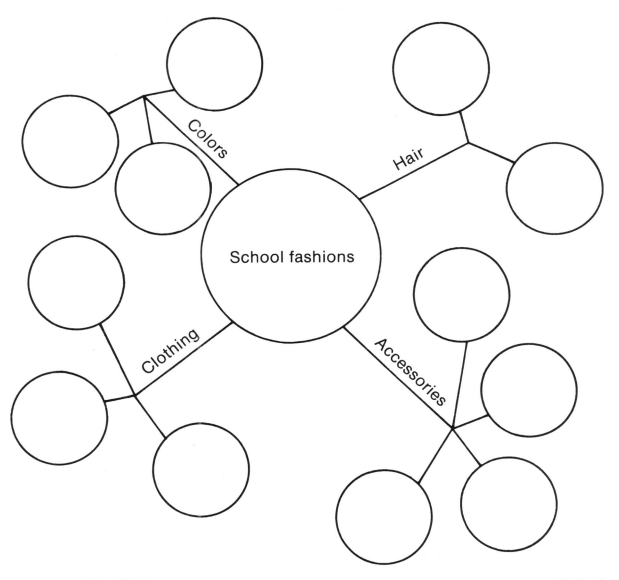

The School Fashion Scene

People wear some crazy things around this school. I saw some girls with

.... on their .... —in public!

At dances there are plenty of ....

and .... The .... are no

.... , either. The other day some were

wearing .... and even .... in their hair.

And the jewelry! Last week I saw ....

So much for the dress code.

Not just girls are creative dressers. In ....

class some guys were sporting ....

It looks as if they .... And the accessories:

.... ! The latest fad is to

.... I guess we

all have different tastes.

Date ....

The School Fashion Scene

....

....

....

....

....

....

....

....

....

....

....

....

....

....

....

....

....

....

....

....

....

Frame 36

This is your chance to create your own web. Your topic is going to be "My Favorite Food." Start by writing the name of your favorite food in the large middle balloon. In the smaller balloons around it, describe your favorite food, explain how it is prepared, mention where and when you first tasted this special food, and then—it's up to you!

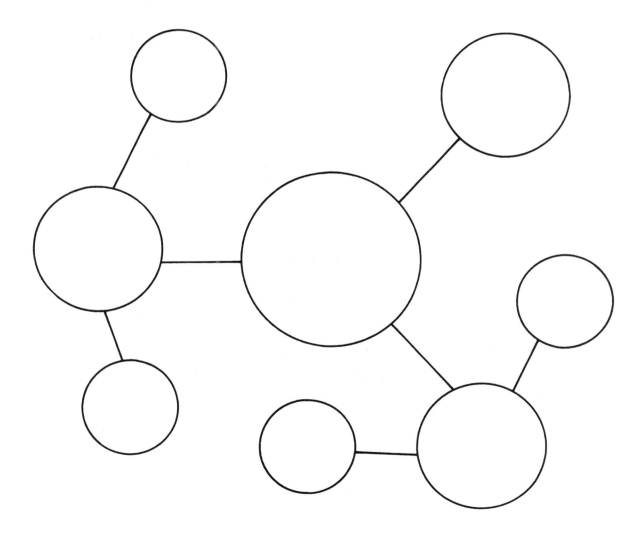

Date ....

My Favorite Food

There are lots of wonderful foods to eat. Some of my favorites are

.... , ... , crunchy

.... , cool .... ,

and hot .... But, if I had to pick

a favorite, it would be .... Delicious

.... is absolutely the ....

The first time I can remember eating ....

was .... I'm not sure who did the cooking, but it may have

been .... , who ....

I loved it then and ....

.... ,

When someone says .... , I say

.... (*You may want to finish the frame by discussing how to prepare your favorite food.*)

Date ....

My Favorite Food

....
....
....
....
....
....
....
....
....
....
....
....
....
....
....
....
....
....
....
....

127   *Writing Frames*

Frame 37

This web and frame give you an opportunity to write about a favorite activity: going to the movies. Complete the web before moving on to the frame. When your frame is finished, ask another student to check it over before you write it in final-draft form. Your last step is to reread your final draft to be sure it is your best work.

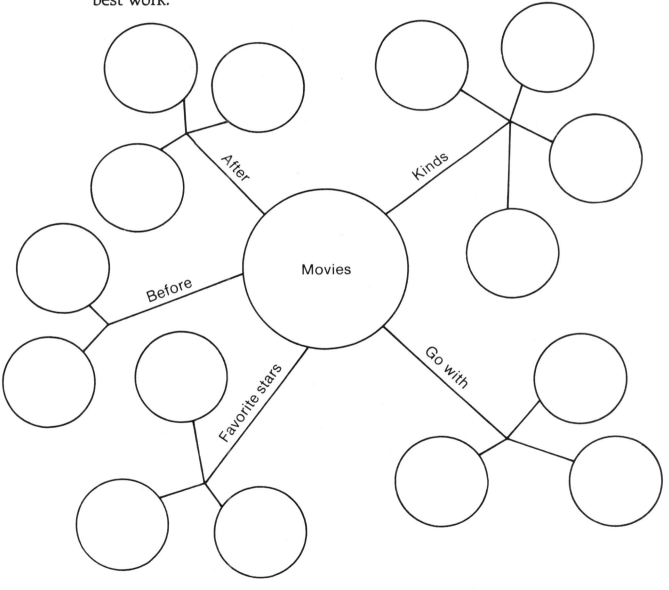

Going to the Movies

One of my favorite activities is going to the movies. I usually go on .... with my .... We take turns picking which kind to see—a .... one, a .... , or maybe a .... We try to go to movies that feature our favorite stars, such as .... or .... There's a new one out with .... that we really want to see. It's about ....

That movie and .... are sure to win Academy awards this year.

We sometimes meet for pizza or .... at .... Then, of course, we buy .... and .... during the movie. We try to sit in the .... of the theater because ....

Afterwards, we sometimes go to .... and talk over the movie. Then we all .... I like going to the movies because ....

Date ....

Going to the Movies

....

....

....

....

....

....

....

....

....

....

....

....

....

....

....

....

....

....

....

....

....

Frame 38

In this web and frame you are to write about winter and spring. Complete the web before moving on to the frame. When your frame is finished, ask another student to check it over before you write it in final draft form. Your last step is to reread your final draft to be sure it is your best work.

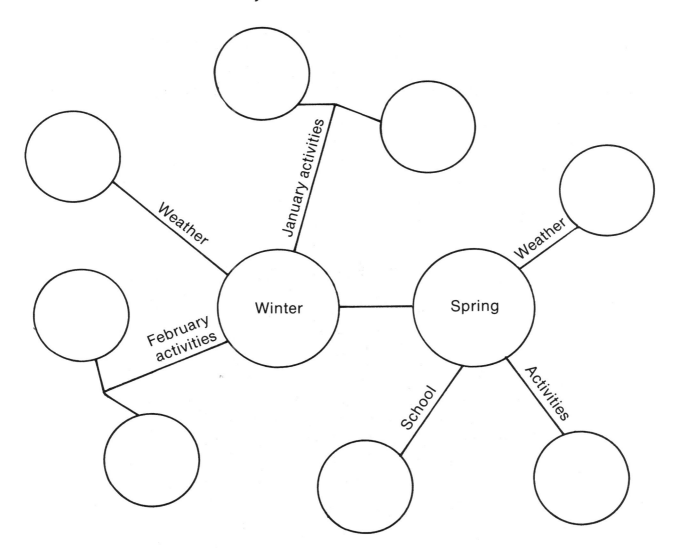

Date ....

Winter and Spring

January is a .... with

.... Most people feel .... and

dread .... February and March are usually

.... I spend most of

my time .... By the end

of March I ....

Spring finally arrives in .... In this

area we have day after day of ....

.... I .... flowers and

trees, and I always notice that ....

One of the great things about spring is ....

.... when my friends and I ....

.... School at this time of the year is

.... and everyone is ....

Date ....

Winter and Spring

....

....

....

....

....

....

....

....

....

....

....

....

....

....

....

....

....

....

....

....

....

Writing Frames

Frame 39

The purpose of this web and frame is to give you a pat on the back for all that you have accomplished. School isn't always easy, and sometimes it is easier to give up than it is to try. In this writing assignment you have a chance to write about things in which you take pride. Don't be modest; everyone needs a little praise!

Complete the web before moving on to the frame. Ask another student for suggestions which might improve your work and then rewrite your material in final-draft form. Remember to read it over to be sure it is your best work.

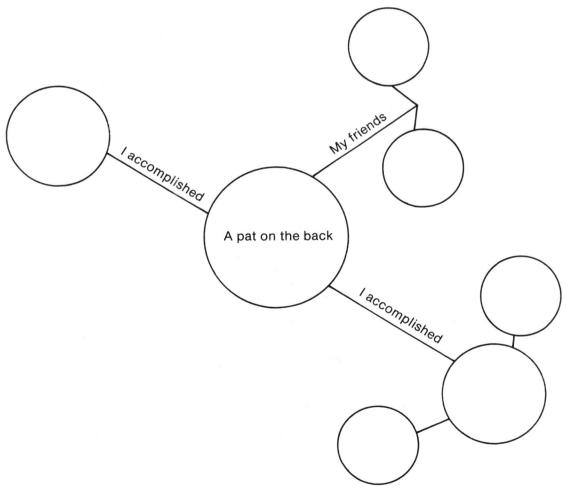

A Pat on the Back

There is no doubt about it, I am proud of ....

.... When I began .... I wasn't

sure I .... , but

now I have proven to myself and everyone else that ....

.... Another thing I am proud of is ....

.... , which may not seem .... to everyone

but makes a difference to me.

I am also proud to have friends like ....

and .... They are the kind of friends who ....

.... They are always ready to ....

.... , which I ....

People need friends because ....

....

I am also proud of ....

.... I guess

I'm pretty lucky to ....

....

Date ....

A Pat on the Back

....

....

....

....

....

....

....

....

....

....

....

....

....

....

....

....

....

....

....

....

Frame 40

This is it, the last frame in the series. In this web and frame you have an opportunity to write about your plans for the coming summer. Remember to expand the web and frame to meet your needs.

When you are finished with the web and frame, ask another student to read over your frame and make suggestions which might improve it. Copy your frame and then reread it. Good luck!

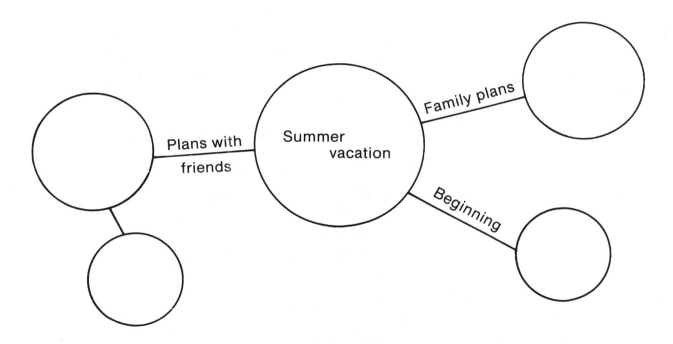

 Writing Frames

Date ....

Summer Vacation

Summer vacation is going to be ....

this year because .... I've

been looking forward to it since ....

At times it seemed as if .... ,

but now it is only ....

During the first few days of vacation I am going to .... in

the morning and spend my afternoons ....

Summer evenings are super because ....

This summer my friends and I plan to ....

....

....

During July/August my family and I will ....

.... We have been doing this every summer for ....

.... and I always ....

....

....

....

Date ....

Summer Vacation

....

....

....

....

....

....

....

....

....

....

....

....

....

....

....

....

....

....

....

....

FINAL EVALUATION

You've done it! You have completed all the frames in this workbook and are now ready to do your final evaluation. Before answering the questions below, arrange your work in chronological order.

Each question is worth 10 points. In order to get any credit, you must finish all parts of a question and your answers must be written in clear sentences. When you finish with the evaluation, total the points for your grade. Good luck!

1. Reread the final draft of Frame 31. On the lines below, write four ideas you mentioned in that composition as possible writing topics for future compositions.

   ....

   ....

   ....

   ....

2. Select one of the topics you mentioned in Question 1 and do a simple web about that topic. Begin with one central balloon and branch off from there.

3. Go back to Question 2. Think about an interesting beginning for a composition on the topic you selected. Write the first sentence for that composition on the lines below.

   ....

   ....

   ....

Final Evaluation

4. In the last 10 compositions you wrote in this series, you were asked to reread your final draft before being sure that you were done. Why do you think this is an important last step?

   . . . .

   . . . .

   . . . .

5. Reread "One Day in the Life of a Student," your third composition for this quarter. Write a good final sentence which tells how a student feels at the end of a school day.

   . . . .

   . . . .

   . . . .

   . . . .

6. Select your favorite composition from this quarter's work. Why is this your favorite? Give at least two specific reasons.

   . . . .

   . . . .

   . . . .

   . . . .

7. Name one way in which your writing has improved this year.

   . . . .

   . . . .

Date . . . .

Final Evaluation

8. Why do you think your writing has improved?

   . . . .

   . . . .

   . . . .

9. What should you do to be sure that your writing continues to improve?

   . . . .

   . . . .

   . . . .

   . . . .

10. Reread the answers you have written to these questions. Check for correct capitalization, spelling, and neatness. Rewrite any answers which are not satisfactory. Write the number of corrections you made on the lines below.

   . . . .

   . . . .

   . . . .

TOTAL POINTS   . . . .

NOTES

NOTES

NOTES